sandi thom

smile... it confuses people

Published by
Wise Publications
14-15 Berners Street, London, W1T 3LJ, UK.

Exclusive distributors:
Music Sales Limited
Distribution Centre, Newmarket Road,
Bury St Edmunds, Suffolk, IP33 3YB, UK.

Music Sales Pty Limited
120 Rothschild Avenue, Rosebery,
NSW 2018, Australia.

Order No. AM986502
ISBN 1-84609-671-5
This book © Copyright 2006 Wise Publications,
a division of Music Sales Limited.

Edited by Ann Farmer.
Music arranged by Jack Long.
Music processed by Paul Ewers Music Design.

Printed in the EU.

www.musicsales.com

sandi thom

smile... it confuses people

Wise Publications
part of The Music Sales Group

London / New York / Paris / Sydney / Copenhagen / Berlin / Madrid / Tokyo

01. when horsepower meant
what it said 6

02. i wish i was a punk rocker
(with flowers in my hair) 12

03. lonely girl 16

04. sunset borderline 21

05. little remedy 26

06. castles 31

07. what if i'm right 36

08. superman 41

09. the human jukebox 46

10. time 51

When Horsepower Meant What It Said

Words & Music by Sandi Thom & Tom Gilbert

1. Caught in the grid - lock, nose to tail a - cross all lanes;

2. I've got a hun - dred hors - es hid - den in be - tween my wheels;

smog near-ly chok - ing me,_____ as the car horns go
but I can't put_____ my foot down and jump_ those fenc - es in

in - sane_____ But they're
the field;_____ be - cause they're

pa - tient-ly wait - ing to get_ their old_ jobs back:_____

car - ry-ing the hu-man race_ proud - ly on_ their_____ backs._____

7

How ea - - si - ly for -gotten, how ea - - si - ly we're led. How hard the path is trod - den from when { horse - pow'r meant what it said. horse - pow'r meant what it

8

May-be we should take a walk and____ talk with the hors - es on___ the___

_ hill._____ And how

ea - - - si-ly____ for - got - ten, how

ea - - si-ly____ we're__ led. How

I Wish I Was A Punk Rocker (With Flowers In My Hair)

Words & Music by Sandi Thom & Tom Gilbert

Oh, I wish I was a punk-rock-er with flo-wers in my hair. In se-ven-ty se-ven and six-ty nine, re-vo-lu-tions was in the air. I was born too late, in-to a world that does-n't care. Oh, I

wish I was a punk - rock - er____ with flo - wers in my____ hair. 1. When the

♩ = 108
(Chords 3° only)

head of state__ did - n't play gui - tar,__ not ev - 'ry - bo - dy drove a car,__ when
(2.) pop stars still re - mained a myth__ and ig - no - rance__ could still__ be bliss, and when
(3.) re - cord shops were still on top__ and vi - nyl was__ all that__ they stocked, and the

*L.H. play 3° only (to *)*

mu - sic real - ly mat - tered and__ when ra - di - o____ was king;__ when ac -
God saved the Queen,__ she turned a whit - er shade of pale.__
su - per - in - fo - high - way was still drift - ing out in space.

13

Lonely Girl

Words & Music by Sandi Thom

1. I some-times see her down by the riv-er, the wa-ter danc-es on her skin;
(2.) late-ly she's been watch-ing the wea-ther, the wea-ther does-n't know what to do;

as she can cap-ti-vate you with her eyes, but she will
'cause some-times, when it's cold out-side, that's

nev-er let you in. And I see
when she's feel-ing blue. He said

through her sad - ness deep with - in her soul;

in the dark she ling - ers like a tear
all she wants to have is some - one she can love

with - out a soul.
to make her whole. And ah,

what a lone - ly girl,

Sunset Borderline

Words & Music by Sandi Thom, Jake Field & Duncan Thompson

To Coda II

Little Remedy

Words & Music by Sandi Thom, Jake Field & Duncan Thompson

1. Some things are meant to be___ the way they're gon-na be,___ 'cause you
2. Some things in this life___ may just pass you by;___ but they're

can't stop time___ or change his-to-ry___
gone for-ev-er in the blink of an eye.___

Castles

Words & Music by Sandi Thom, Tom Gilbert & Jake Field

What If I'm Right

Words & Music by Sandi Thom & Tom Gilbert

You'll be true, and be faith-ful too; but I've

got my doubts, and what if I'm right?

What if I'm right?

Superman

Words & Music by Sandi Thom & Tom Gilbert

Mm,

mm

1. Some of us are reach-ing for star-dust, and
(2.) some of us stand in the spot-light,
(3.) some of us want sil-ver lin - ings,

43

The Human Jukebox

Words & Music by Sandi Thom & Tom Gilbert

juke- box; he plays se - cond- hand rock- 'n'- roll. Yeah, they

call him the hu - man juke- box; you know that he's heal - ing hearts

with his soul.

And they're ka - ra - o - ke kings for the eve - ning; it's the

Time

Words & Music by Sandi Thom & Simon Perry

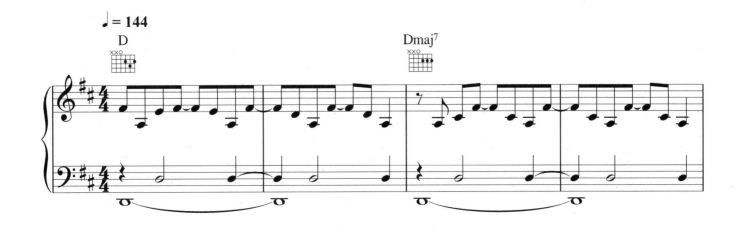

1. Rol - ler skates and bum - ble bees; hold - ing hands and graz - ing knees;
2. Skiv - ing French and steal - ing Mars; hang - ing out in Ro - sie's Bar;
3. Up and down to Liv - er - pool; learn - ing lines to play the fool;

G   Gm

dress - ing up___ and fall - ing down;___ Paul and Mike___ are com - ing round;___
get - ting changed straight af - ter school;___ smok - ing fags___ and play - ing pool;___
hang - ing out___ at Han-nah's Bar;___ got too drunk to drive___ the car;___ and

D   Dmaj⁷

be - ing good___ to stay___ up late;___ for - got to shut___ the gar - den gate;___
rain - bow gath - ered ov - er me,___ but I___ like Gra - ham Con - nel - ly;___
ev - en though I'd love___ to stay,___ it's time to work, not time to play; and

G   Gm

build a house___ up in a tree,___ been mak - ing plans___ since I___ was three...
get - ting caught in some - one's car;___ "this time, kid, you've gone___ too far"... 'Cause
ev - en though you're now___ for me, soon you'll be a me - mo - ry...